PRACTICE PAPERS FOR CREDIT MATHEMATICS

by

P.W. Westwood,
Principal Teacher of Mathematics,
Kirkcaldy High School

ISBN 0 7169 8018 5

ROBERT GIBSON · Publisher
17 Fitzroy Place, Glasgow, G3 7SF, Scotland, U.K.
www.gibson-books.co.uk

PREFACE

These practice examination papers were devised by the author to give candidates sitting the National Qualifications Credit Level Mathematics Examination extra practice with working through exam papers. This is a popular and useful way of preparing for the exam and it can be useful to set yourself 55 minutes for Paper 1 and 80 minutes for Paper 2. You can revise a particular type of question by referring to the question analysis table at the back of this book.

MATHEMATICS

STANDARD GRADE

Credit Level

INSTRUCTIONS TO CANDIDATES

Paper 1 — Non-calculator

Time: 55 minutes

1. **You may <u>not</u> use a calculator**.

2. Answer as many questions as you can.

3. Full credit will be given only where the solution contains appropriate working.

Paper 2

Time: 80 minutes

1. **You may use a calculator**.

2. Answer as many questions as you can.

3. Full credit will be given only where the solution contains appropriate working.

FORMULAE LIST

The roots of $ax^2 + bx + c = 0$ are $x = \dfrac{-b \pm \sqrt{b^2 - 4ac}}{2a}$

Sine rule: $\dfrac{a}{\sin A} = \dfrac{b}{\sin B} = \dfrac{c}{\sin C}$

Cosine rule: $a^2 = b^2 + c^2 - 2bc \cos A$ or $\cos A = \dfrac{b^2 + c^2 - a^2}{2bc}$

Area of a triangle: Area $= \dfrac{1}{2} ab \sin C$

Volume of a cylinder: Volume $= \pi r^2 h$

Sample standard deviation: $s = \sqrt{\dfrac{\Sigma(x - \bar{x})^2}{n - 1}} = \sqrt{\dfrac{\Sigma x^2 - (\Sigma x)^2 / n}{n - 1}}$, where n is the sample size.

PRACTICE PAPER A

C

Paper 1

Non-calculator

Refer to page 3 for Instructions to Candidates

	KU	RE

1. Evaluate $\quad 15 \cdot 2 - 3 \cdot 1 \times 6 \cdot 1 + 10 \cdot 3$ — **2**

2. Evaluate $\quad 1\frac{3}{5} + 2\frac{2}{3}$ — **2**

3. Express $(3 \cdot 4 \times 10^5) \times (4 \cdot 5 \times 10^3)$ in standard form
   (i.e. $a \times 10^n$, $1 \le a < 10$, n an integer). — **2**

4. The functions f and g are given by
   $f(x) = 2x^3 - 1$ and $g(x) = 3x^2 + 1$.

   Find $\quad f(2), \quad g(-1), \quad$ and $f(g(-1))$ — **4**

5. Solve $\quad 3(x-1) - 1 < 2(x+1)$ — **4**

6. Simplify $\quad \dfrac{2x^2 + 6x}{x^2 - 9}$ — **3**

7. The formula $\dfrac{1}{f} = \dfrac{1}{u} + \dfrac{1}{v}$ occurs in geometrical optics.

   Express the formula in the form $f =$ — **3**

5

8. A publisher produces a new series of maths books and the design chosen to appear on the front cover consists of an array of red and yellow discs as shown.

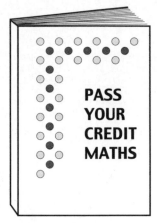

The yellow discs are arranged in squares and the red discs appear in the centre of such a square, but at either end of the pattern the artist omits one yellow disc from the inner row as shown.

(a) Show that in the size of the pattern illustrated the number of yellow discs is twice the number of red ones.

(b) Show that the number of yellow discs is always twice the number of red ones for all sizes of this pattern. [Let there be *n* red discs in the top row and *m* red discs in the column down the side.]

(c) An apprentice in the firm calculated that if all the books printed in the first run were sold, exactly one million discs (red and yellow together) would have been sold. Comment on the truth of this statement.

9. A poster measuring $18'' \times 12''$ is to be mounted on a sheet of card so that

(a) the width of the resulting card border is the same on all four sides, and

(b) the areas of the frame and border are equal.

Calculate the width of the border.

10.

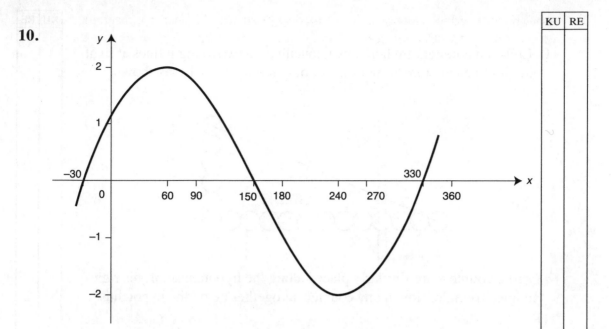

The diagram shows part of the graph of the function f given by $f(x) = a \cos(x + b)^\circ$.

Find the values of a and b.

2

11. Eighteen counters are laid down, touching, in two straight lines at right angles to each other to make a row of 6 and a row of 13, as shown.

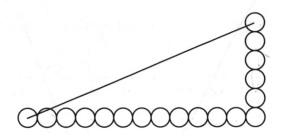

(a) More counters are similarly placed along the hypotenuse of this right-angled triangle. How many counters altogether lie on the hypotenuse?

2

The three counters at the vertices are red, the other four on the shortest side are blue, the other eleven on 'the base' are green and the remaining counters on the hypotenuse are yellow.

(b) One of these counters is chosen at random. What is the probability that it is yellow?

3

(c) If a red counter is chosen and not put back, what is the probability that a second counter chosen at random is also red?

2

[END OF QUESTION PAPER]

PRACTICE TEST A

C

Paper 2

Refer to page 3 for Instructions to Candidates

1. Write down the equation of the line AB which passes through A(0, 3) and B(6, 0).

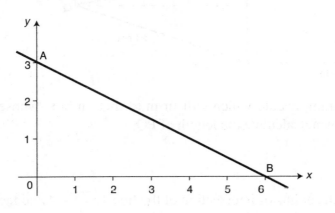

2. The horsepower (H.P.) being developed by an engine varies jointly as the tractive effort (T) of the engine and the speed (v) at which it is moving. If H.P. = 16 when $T = 200$ and $v = 44$, find the formula for H.P. in terms of T and v.

3. A rectangular room measuring 7·9 m × 5·6 m is to be carpeted with self-coloured cord carpet cut from a large roll of width 2 m.

    Illustrate the most economical method of carpeting this room (with the weave all running in the same direction) stating the least length of carpet off the roll that would need to be purchased.

4. Write down the period of each of these functions
    (i) $\sin \frac{1}{2}x^\circ$
    (ii) $\cos 3x^\circ$
    (iii) $\tan (x - 45)^\circ$.

KU	RE
3	
4	
	6
3	

5.

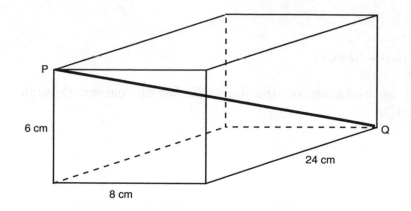

PQ is the longest knitting needle which will fit in to this tin box, whose measurements are shown. Calculate the length of PQ.

4

6. The x-coordinates of the points of intersection of the line $4y = x + 4$ and the curve $xy = 8$ can be found from the solution of the equation $\dfrac{x+4}{4} = \dfrac{8}{x}$. Solve this equation for x.

4

7.

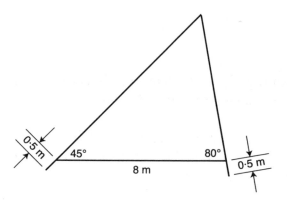

An architect is designing a time-share luxury chalet, which is to measure 8 m from back to front, and whose front wall is to be south facing. The front part of the ridged roof is to be inclined at 45° to the horizontal to obtain maximum benefit from the solar panels, and the rear part of the roof is to be inclined at 80° to the horizontal to accommodate the water tanks in the roof space. Calculate the longest length of rafter that will be required, if each projects half a metre beyond the wall as shown.

3

8. John is twice his sister Mary's age at present.

In three year's time, John will only be one and half times Mary's age.

Let Mary's age now be x years. Form an equation in x, solve it, and hence determine how old John was when Mary was born.

6

9. A point source of light, A, is shone vertically on to a mirror at B and is reflected to a point C on the horizontal plane through A. Calculate the size of $A\hat{B}C$ if AB = 2 m and AC = 42 mm.

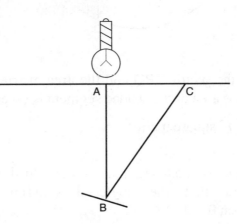

Given that the line through B perpendicular to the mirror bisects the angle between the rays of light, calculate the angle at which the mirror is inclined to the horizontal.

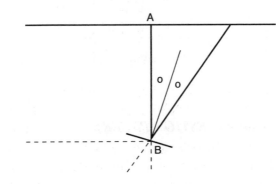

6

10. This diagram represents a circular swimming pool, of radius r metres, with the shaded seqment roped off for the users of the diving board.

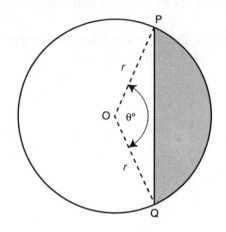

(a) Find the area of the sector OPQ and the area of triangle OPQ, and hence show that the area of the shaded segment is given by

$$\left(\frac{\theta\pi}{360} - \frac{1}{2} \sin \theta \right) r^2 \text{ square metres.}$$

(b) If the area of the shaded segment is one third of the area of the circle, show that the angle θ satisfies the equation $\pi(\theta - 120) - 180 \sin \theta = 0$.

(c) Show that this equation has a root between 149 and 150, and find it correct to one decimal place.

[END OF QUESTION PAPER]

PRACTICE PAPER B

C

Paper 1

Non-calculator

Refer to page 3 for Instructions to Candidates

	KU	RE

1. Between which two consecutive integers does $\sqrt{333}$ lie?

   KU: 2

2. Evaluate $2\frac{2}{3} \times 1\frac{1}{8}$

   KU: 2

3. Solve $x - 3 - \dfrac{x-4}{3} = 5$

   RE: 3

4. Given that P varies as the square of m, complete this table:

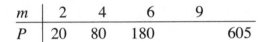

m	2	4	6	9	
P	20	80	180		605

   RE: 3

5.

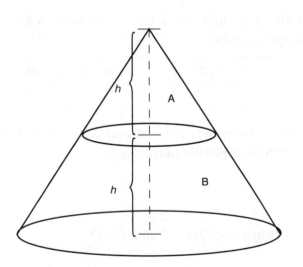

   A cone of height $2h$ is cut into two parts A and B so that Part A is a cone of height h. If the volume of part A is 15 cm³, calculate of volume of part B.

   RE: 4

6. John and Sally have equal amounts of money in their possession.

John has the same number of 5p pieces as Sally has 2p pieces.

John also has eight 1p coins and Sally fourteen 1p coins.

How much money does each have?

4

7.

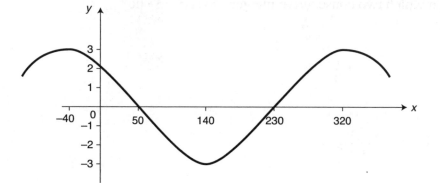

This diagram shows part of the graph of $y = a \cos (x + b)°$.

Find the values of a and b.

2

8. The waist sizes of the jeans sold one Saturday morning in *Keen on Jeans* are given in this frequency table.

Size (inches)	29	30	31	32	33	34	35	36	37	38
Frequency	2	3	2	4	3	4	5	3	2	1

Construct a cumulative frequency column and use it to find the median waist size and the semi-interquartile range.

4

9. Evaluate $\dfrac{p^2 - 4qr}{r}$ when $p = -7$, $r = 2$ and $q = -3$.

2

14

10. A craft shop sells pot stands made of wood with a tiled pattern inlaid in the centre. One range of pot stands of different sizes uses red and blue tiles each 5 mm square to produce the design shown below. The first two sizes in the range are shown, the shaded tiles being red and the unshaded being blue.

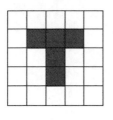

(a) Sketch the third pot stand in this range, whose T is three times as broad as the first T.

(b) Complete this table.

	Size 1	Size 2	Size 3
Number of red tiles			
Number of blue tiles			

(c) Find in its simplest form an expression for the number of blue tiles required to make the pot stand of size n.

11. The acute angle x is such that $\tan x = \dfrac{2}{3}$.

(a) Express the value of $\sin x$ with a rational denominator.

(b) Showing your working, evaluate $\sin^2 x + \cos^2 x$.

12. Determine the equation of the parabola which passes through the points $(-1, 0), (0, 3)$ and $(3, 0)$.

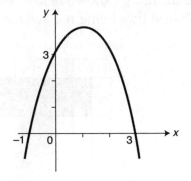

3

[END OF QUESTION PAPER]

PRACTICE PAPER B

C

Paper 2

Refer to page 3 for Instructions to Candidates

	KU	RE

1. Solve $\begin{cases} 3x - 4y = 25 \\ 5x + 2y = 7 \end{cases}$

    KU: 4

2. Make q the subject of the formula $p = \dfrac{q}{r - q}$.

    KU: 4

3. The moment of inertia, I, of a uniform circular disc varies jointly as the mass, m, of the disc and the square of the radius, r, of the disc.

    (a) Find the relationship between I, m and r, if $I = 16$ when $m = 8$ and $r = 2$.

    KU: 4

    (b) A disc of mass m_1 and radius r_1 has a moment of inertia I_1.
    A second disc of mass m_2 and radius r_2 has a moment of inertia I_2.
    If $I_2 = 2I_1$, find an expression for the ratio $r_1 : r_2$.

    RE: 4

4. Solve $3 \cos x° - 1 = 0$ for $0 < x < 180$

    KU: 2

5. Express $\dfrac{1}{x(x + 2)} + \dfrac{1}{x(x - 2)}$ as a single fraction in its simplest form.

    KU: 4

6.

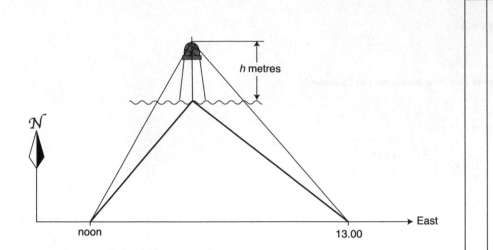

A ship is sailing due east at 6 km / h.
At noon the ship's crew observe a lighthouse on a bearing of 035°.
At 13:00 the lighthouse lies on a bearing of 310°.

Calculate

(a) the distance between the ship and the lighthouse at noon,

(b) the height, h metres, of the top of the lighthouse above sea level, given that at noon the crew measured its angle of elevation to be 0·8°,

(c) the angle of elevation of the top of the lighthouse as seen from the ship at 13:00.

4

4

4

18

7.

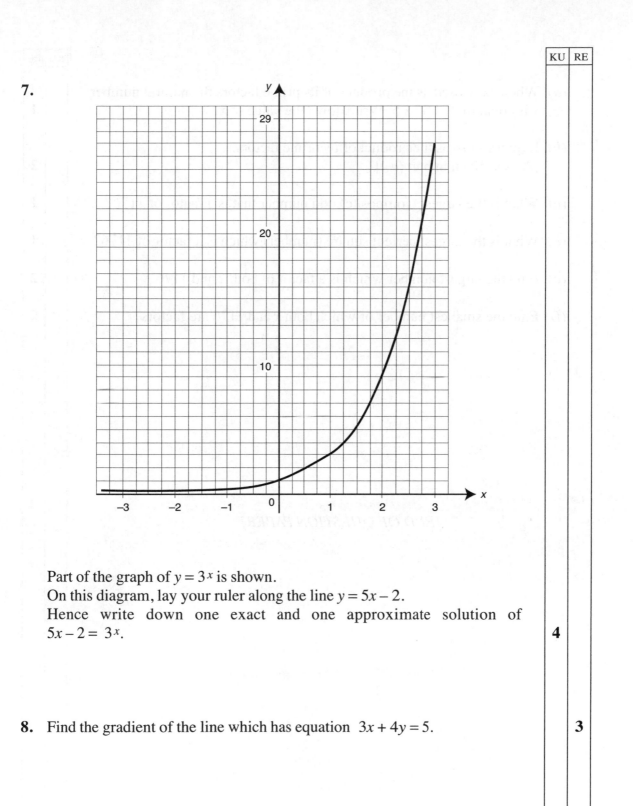

Part of the graph of $y = 3^x$ is shown.

On this diagram, lay your ruler along the line $y = 5x - 2$.

Hence write down one exact and one approximate solution of $5x - 2 = 3^x$.

8. Find the gradient of the line which has equation $3x + 4y = 5$.

9. *(a)* When expressed as the product of its prime factors the natural number
x is equal to $2^2 \times 3^2 \times 5$. Write down the value of *x*.

    1

(b) Express 1176 as the product of its prime factors.
[As *x* is given in part *(a)*.]

    2

(c) What is the largest (composite) odd number that is a factor of 1176?

    1

(d) What is the largest perfect square (number) which is a factor of 1176?

    1

(e) Find the largest number which is a factor of both *x* and 1176.

    2

(f) Find the smallest number of which both *x* and 1176 are factors.

    2

[END OF QUESTION PAPER]

PRACTICE PAPER C

C

Paper 1

Non-calculator

Refer to page 3 for Instructions to Candidates

	KU	RE

1. Evaluate $\quad 72{\cdot}3 - 3{\cdot}7 \times 2$ — KU **2**

2. Express $\quad 3\dfrac{3}{4} - 1\dfrac{5}{12}\quad$ as a single fraction. — KU **2**

3. Express $\quad 2\dfrac{7}{10} \div 3\dfrac{3}{5}\quad$ as a single fraction. — KU **2**

4. Solve $\quad \begin{cases} 5x + 6y = 2 \\ 10y - 7x = 11 \end{cases}$ — KU **5**

5. Make x the subject of the formula $\quad v = w\,\sqrt{a^2 - x^2}$ — KU **4**

6. When the leading yacht A in a race is rounding the marker buoy at the turn, the second yacht B is observed to be half a mile away on a bearing of 095°. At this instant, what is the bearing of A from B? — KU **2**

7. The **weight** of an astronaut in the earth's gravitational field varies as the mass of the astronaut and inversely as the square of his distance from the centre of the earth. Astronaut A is circling the earth at a height R above the earth's surface where R is the length of the radius of the earth. Astronaut B is the same mass as A and is circling the earth at a height of $2R$ above the earth's surface. Calculate the ratio of the weight of astronaut A to the weight of astronaut B.

4

8.

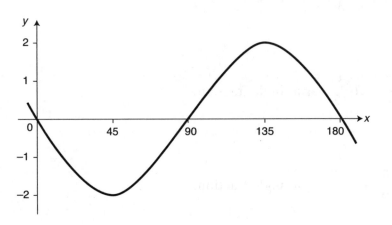

This diagram shows part of the graph of the function f given by $f(x) = a \sin bx°$. Find the values of a and b.

2

9. Solve $\left(\dfrac{x}{9}\right)^2 = \dfrac{-3}{x^3}$

3

10. In rectangle PQRS, PQ = x cm and PS = 2 cm.

AB divides PQRS into two smaller rectangles such that

(i) SB = 3 cm   and

(ii) the rectangles PQRS and ABRQ are similar.

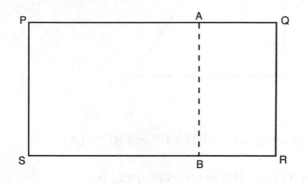

By considering the ratios of corresponding sides of the similar figures, construct an equation for x and solve it.

5

11.

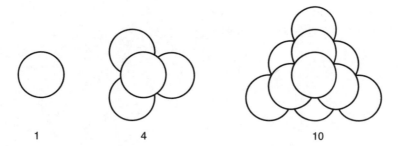

| 1 | 4 | 10 |

With one layer, there is one cannonball in the pyramid.
With two layers, there are 4 cannonballs in the pyramid.
With three layers, there are 10 cannonballs in the pyramid.

How many cannonballs are in the pyramid with 4 layers?
How many cannonballs are in the pyramid with 5 layers?

3

12.

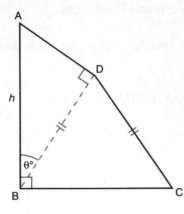

ABCD is a sail of height h metres with $\hat{ABD} = \theta°$ and $BD = DC$.

(a) Express the lengths of AD and BD in terms of h and θ.

(b) Show that $\hat{BDC} = 2\theta$.

(c) Hence, show that the area, A square metres, of the sail is given by

$$A = \frac{1}{2} h^2 \cos \theta° [\sin \theta° + \cos \theta°. \sin 2\theta°]$$

[END OF QUESTION PAPER]

PRACTICE PAPER C

C

Paper 2

Refer to page 3 for Instructions to Candidates

	KU	RE

1. Water is flowing through a horizontal 26-inch diameter pipe. The width of the water surface is 24 inches. Calculate the depth of the water.

   Is this the only possible answer? — **4**

2. Calculate the compound interest on £500 for three years at 5% per annum. — **4**

3. When two dice are rolled, the array below illustrates all the possible outcomes.

1, 1	1, 2	1, 3	1, 4	1, 5	1, 6
2, 1	2, 2	2, 3	2, 4	2, 5	2, 6
3, 1	3, 2	3, 3	3, 4	3, 5	3, 6
4, 1	4, 2	4, 3	4, 4	4, 5	4, 6
5, 1	5, 2	5, 3	5, 4	5, 5	5, 6
6, 1	6, 2	6, 3	6, 4	6, 5	6, 6

   Coloured labels are stuck on the faces of two dice, so that the number 1s are covered red, numbers 2 and 3 are covered blue and numbers 4, 5, 6 are covered yellow.

   (a) Construct an array similar to the one shown to illustrate all the possible outcomes of rolling these two coloured dice. — **2**

   (b) If these two dice were rolled 360 times, how often would you expect to obtain two reds? — **2**

   (c) Which is the more likely, obtaining at least one red, or both dice being the same colour? — **3**

25

4. The graph shown has equation $y = x^2 - 2x - 15$.

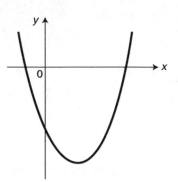

(a) Find the coordinates of the three points where the graph cuts the x- and y-axes.

(b) Find the coordinates of the minimum turning point.

5. Calculate the area of a triangular field, the sides of which measure 110 m, 152 m and 207 m.

6.

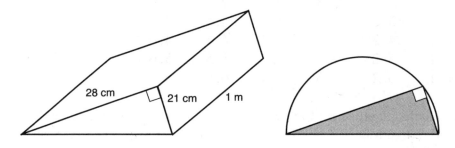

A museum curator designs a display case 1 m long for a historic document by constructing a triangular prism whose cross-section is a right-angled triangle with shorter sides of 21 cm and 28 cm. This is enclosed within a perspex case whose cross section is semi-circular as shown. If the ends are also sealed with semi-circular sheets of perspex, calculate, in litres, the volume of air enclosed within the display case.

7. A box contains numerous identical bolts and identical nuts.

Eleven bolts and seven nuts have a mass of 167 g.

Eight bolts and nine nuts have a mass of 141 g.

Find the mass of ten bolts and eight nuts.

8.

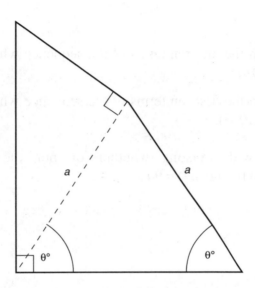

The area, A square metres, of this sail is given by
$$A = \frac{1}{2}\, a^2\, [\sin 2\theta° + \tan(90 - \theta)°]$$
where a metres is the length of the side shown.

Find the value of a for which the area is 11·5 m² and $\theta = 60°$. [Answer correct to 2 significant figures.]

9. The function f is defined by the rule $f(n)$ is the largest whole number which is a perfect square and which is less than or equal to n.

(a) Find

    (i) $f(4 \cdot 9)$

    (ii) $f(49)$

    (iii) $f(490)$ **3**

(b) (i) Write down the first ten terms of the sequence whose n^{th} term is given by $10n^2$.   **2**

    (ii) Write down the first ten terms of the sequence whose n^{th} term is given by $f(10n^2)$.   **2**

(c) Hence state with reasons whether or not the formula for $f(10n^2)$ is given by $f(10n^2) = 9n^2$.   **2**

[END OF QUESTION PAPER

PRACTICE PAPER D

C

Paper 1
Non-calculator

Refer to page 3 for Instructions to Candidates

	KU	RE

1. Between which two consecutive integers does $\sqrt[3]{8064}$ lie?

   KU: 2

2. Evaluate $1{\cdot}335 \div 1{\cdot}5$

   KU: 2

3. Express $(6{\cdot}3 \times 10^2) \div (0{\cdot}7 \times 10^{-1})$ in standard form
   (i.e., $a \times 10^n$, $1 \le a < 10$, n an integer).

   KU: 2

4. An experiment establishes that H and t are connected by a linear relationship. It is known that $H = 1$ when $t = 0$ and that the gradient of the graph is $\dfrac{2}{3}$.

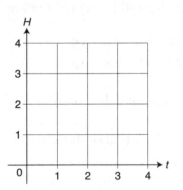

   Make a rough copy of this coordinate diagram and add the graph of the line.

   KU: 2

5. Calculate (as an exact multiple of π) the area of the circle.

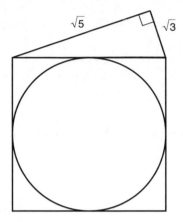

5

6. *(a)* Expand $\left[a^{\frac{1}{2}} + a^{-\frac{1}{2}} \right]^2$

3

(b) Find the exact value of this expression when $a = 16$.

1

7. A class of 20 pupils was asked to translate a long article from *Der Stern*. The number of mistakes made by each pupil is recorded below.

$$
\begin{array}{cccccccccc}
23 & 7 & 31 & 9 & 4 & 14 & 35 & 30 & 6 & 15 \\
8 & 31 & 5 & 26 & 13 & 10 & 25 & 10 & 8 & 30
\end{array}
$$

(a) Find the median number of mistakes and the quartiles.

3

(b) Calculate the mean and standard deviation of those scores which were better than the median score.

4

(c) Given that the scores which were worse than the median had a mean of 26 and a standard deviation of about 7, write down any differences between these two distributions.

2

30

8.

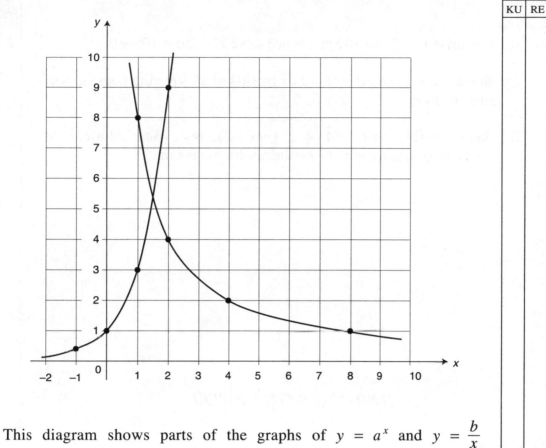

This diagram shows parts of the graphs of $y = a^x$ and $y = \dfrac{b}{x}$ $(a > 1, b > 0)$.

Find the values of a and b.

9. Caledonian Confectioners produce lumps of fudge in the shape of cuboids measuring $36\ \text{mm} \times 36\ \text{mm} \times 18\ \text{mm}$.

It is decided that these lumps look too thin and the height should be increased to 32 mm. If the new shaped lumps are to contain the same amount of fudge as the old ones, find the length of the side of the square base.

10. *(a)* Factorise $x^2 - 29x + 100$ and hence solve $x^2 - 29x + 100 = 0$.

(b) Solve the equation $x - 10 = 3\sqrt{x}$ by first of all squaring both sides of this equation.

(c) Remembering that $\sqrt{4} = 2$ (not –2), test your solutions of $x - 10 = 3\sqrt{x}$, and comment on the results you obtain.

KU **2**

RE **3**

RE **3**

[END OF QUESTION PAPER]

PRACTICE PAPER D

C

Paper 2

Refer to page 3 for Instructions to Candidates

KU	RE

1. The number of rabbits in Dura Den was estimated to increase by 12% over a year. If there are 200 rabbits this year and they increase at the estimated rate, how many years will it take for the rabbit population to double?

    4

2. Make h the subject of the formula $A = 2\pi r[r + h]$.

    3

3. Two yachts leave Arbroath harbour at noon.

    The *Bolero* sails at 3 knots on the bearing 050°.

    The *Catalan* sails at 4 knots on the bearing 100°.

    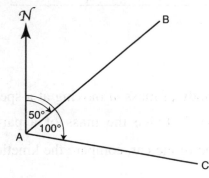

    How far apart are they at 1 p.m.?

    3

4. *(a)* A single cube is made from 8 ball joints and 12 tie rods as shown.

A composite cube consisting of eight of the above cubes is also constructed as shown.

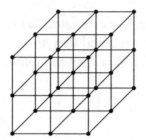

How many ball joints and tie rods are required for this cube?

(b) Complete this table for a set of such cubes.

number of single cubes	1	8	27	n^3
number of ball joints	8			
number of tie rods	12			

5. The kinetic energy of a body of mass m moving at a speed v is given by $\frac{1}{2} mv^2$. If a certain lorry is twice the mass of a particular car, and travelling at half the speed of the car, compare the kinetic energies of the vehicles.

2

5

3

6. *(a)* Calculate the area of this trapezium.

(b) Hence calculate the volume of this platinum bar.
[Volume of a prism = (area of end) × (length).]

(c) If each cubic centimetre of platinum has a mass of 21·5 g, how many kilograms are in the whole ingot of platinum?

(d) In order to smuggle this platinum out of the country under 008's nose, Plattythumb has this ingot melted down and made into similar bars of these dimensions.

How many of the smaller ingots would be obtained from the original?

7. The check-out attendants in Bill Hi's store are instructed to give customers their change using as few coins as possible, e.g., two ten-pence pieces would never be used because a twenty-pence piece would be better. The tills are kept stocked with adequate supplies of each value of coin.

Find the four amounts of change less than 30p for which exactly four coins are required.

8. Express $1 + \dfrac{2x}{(x-1)^2}$ as a single fraction in its simplest form.

9. A flag-pole at a Scout camp is supported by guy ropes.

(a) One of the guys is pegged 2·70 m from the foot of the flag-pole and makes an angle of 63° with the level ground.

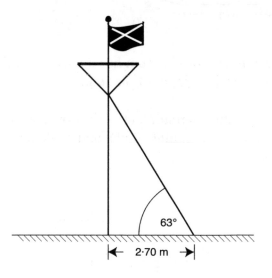

Calculate the height of the point on the flag-pole to which the other end of this guy rope is attached.

(b) A piece of wire of length 3·29 m is used as a radio ariel and installed as shown.

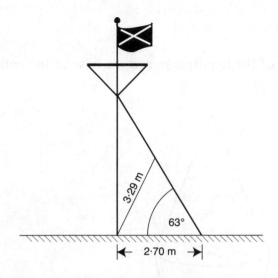

Calculate the angle between the wire and the ground.

3

10. The circumference of Andrew's cycle wheel is 20 cm larger than that of Billy's. Write down an equation to express this mathematically. In cycling 200 m Andrew's wheels complete 50 fewer revolutions than Billy's. Find a second equation (using the same letters as your first one) and hence find the circumference of each wheel.

6

11. The volume, $V \text{ cm}^3$, of the plumb bob shown is given by

$$V = \frac{\pi r^2}{3} [h + 2r]$$

where r cm is the radius of the hemisphere and the base of the cone, and h cm is the height of the cone.

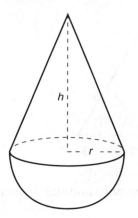

When $r = 2$, what value of h is required to produce a volume of 40 cm^3? Answer correct to the nearest mm.

4

[END OF QUESTION PAPER]

PRACTICE PAPER E

C

Paper 1
Non-calculator

Refer to page 3 for Instructions to Candidates

	KU	RE

1. Evaluate $5 \cdot 78 \div 1 \cdot 7$

2

2. Evaluate $6\frac{2}{7} \div 1\frac{5}{6}$

2

3. Express $\sqrt{1\frac{24}{25}}$ as a mixed number.

2

4. If $R = p^3 + 2q^2$, find R when $p = -4$ and $q = -6$.

2

5. Solve $\frac{5x-3}{2} - \frac{x+2}{3} = 13$

3

6. Calculate the value of x as a surd in its simplest form.

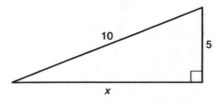

3

7. Football teams score 3 points for a win, one point for a draw and none for losing. With 5 games to go to the end of the season, Boglily Bluebell have 38 points but hope to improve on last season's total of 44. List the different combinations of wins, draws or losses which would allow them to achieve their aim.

4

8. Given $f(x) = 2^x + \dfrac{2}{x}$, evaluate $f(1) - f(-1)$.

3

9. A chip shop sells its chips contained in cardboard cones.

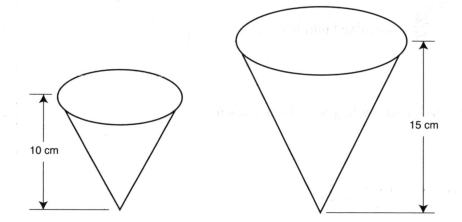

10 cm

15 cm

There are two sizes of cone which are similar in shape. The smaller cone is 10 cm high and has a volume of 240 ml. If the larger cone is 15 cm high, what is its volume?

3

10. The potential energy of a body of mass m kilograms at a height of h metres is given by the expression mgh where g m/s^2 is the acceleration due to gravity.

Express the potential energy of a body of mass $\sqrt{g}$ kg at a height of g metres in the form g^x.

11. Some golfers failed to "make the cut" in a local golf competition. The number of strokes that they were "over par" were as follows.

$$18 \quad 19 \quad 21 \quad 8 \quad 27 \quad 11 \quad 20 \quad 25 \quad 9$$
$$35 \quad 18 \quad 23 \quad 14 \quad 29 \quad 30 \quad 20 \quad 25$$

(a) Construct a box plot for this data.

(b) The box plot for the corresponding results of the same players the previous year looked like this:

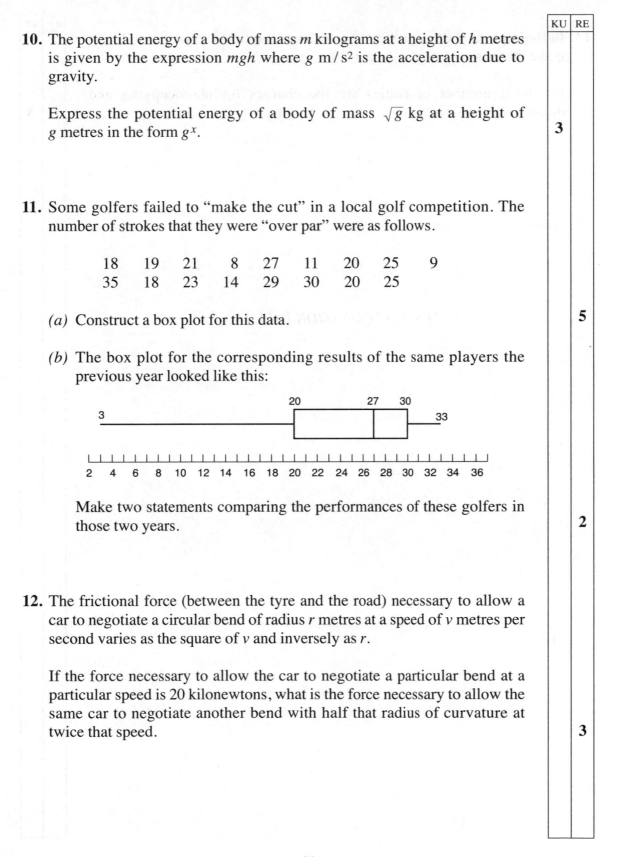

Make two statements comparing the performances of these golfers in those two years.

12. The frictional force (between the tyre and the road) necessary to allow a car to negotiate a circular bend of radius r metres at a speed of v metres per second varies as the square of v and inversely as r.

If the force necessary to allow the car to negotiate a particular bend at a particular speed is 20 kilonewtons, what is the force necessary to allow the same car to negotiate another bend with half that radius of curvature at twice that speed.

KU RE

3

5

2

3

13. In Reprint, photocopies cost 5p each and duplicator copies cost 20p to make the master skin plus 1p per copy.

For what number of copies are the charges for photocopying and duplicating the same?

[END OF QUESTION PAPER]

PRACTICE PAPER E

C

Paper 2

Refer to page 3 for Instructions to Candidates

	KU	RE

1. A gardener draws a plan of his garden on which all lengths are $\dfrac{1}{200}$ of their actual size. He plans a fish pond with an area on the plan of 100 mm². What area of garden would this occupy?

    3

2. A cuboid measures 5 cm × 7 cm × 4 cm.

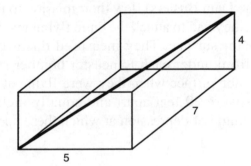

   Calculate the length of a space diagonal and express your answer as a surd in its simplest form.

    4

3. Simplify $\quad \dfrac{y^{\frac{1}{2}} \times y^{\frac{1}{3}}}{y^{-1}}$

    3

4. A survey of 160 randomly chosen pupils in a school asked which TV channel they watched most often. The results are shown below.

	BBC1	BBC2	ITV	CH4	CH5
S1–S3	20	11	28	16	5
S4–S6	23	14	17	20	6

(a) What is the probability that one of these pupils chosen at random

    (i) watches CH5 the most,

    (ii) does not watch a BBC channel the most.

(b) If there were 1120 pupils in the school altogether, how many S4–S6 pupils would you expect to watch CH4 the most?

5. When 617 Squadron (The Dam Busters) flew their mission to the Moehne Dam on 17th May, 1943, they had to attack the dam, flying level at a height of 60 feet above the water surface. They measured this accurately by shining two spotlights from under each Lancaster bomber so that their beams touched on the water surface when they were flying at the correct height. If the spotlights were 20 feet apart and equally inclined to the horizontal, calculate the angle of depression at which these spotlights had to be fixed.

6. Simplify $\dfrac{x^2 + x}{2} \div \dfrac{x^2 - x}{3}$

7. The dining table in a luxury residential caravan is in the shape of a circle centre O of radius 1 m with a segment bounded by the chord AB removed so that $\stackrel{\wedge}{AOB}$ is a right angle. AB fits against the wall.

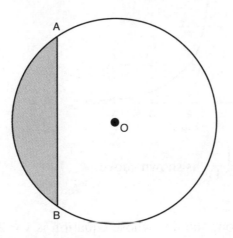

(a) Calculate the area of the top of this table.

4

(b) There is a table mat which fits exactly over the table. The edge of this mat is stitched with protective tape all round its edge. Calculate the length of tape required.

3

8.

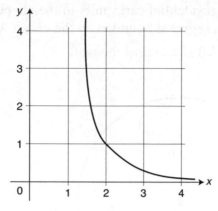

Part of the graph of $y = \dfrac{1}{(x-1)^2}$ is shown above.

(a) By laying your ruler along the line whose equation is $y = 2x$, find an approximate solution of $2x = \dfrac{1}{(x-1)^2}$.

2

(b) Find this root correct to 3 significant figures.

4

9. It is required that the area of this sail shown is at least 7 m².

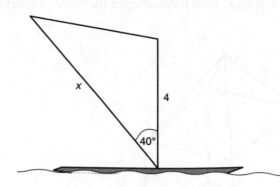

(a) Calculate the least possible length of *x*.

(b) For this value of *x*, calculate the length of the third side.

3

3

10. The lift cage in a modern shopping complex consists of a stainless steel frame and glass faces. It is in the shape of a cube of side 2 m with a square pyramid top and bottom, each edge also measuring 2 m. A sheet steel floor forms the base of the cube.

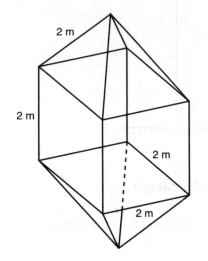

Calculate:

(a) the total length of stainless steel framing used;

2

(b) the area of glass used;

4

(c) the total volume of the lift cage.

$$\left[\text{Volume of pyramid} \ = \ \frac{1}{3} \ (\text{area of base}) \times \text{height.} \right]$$

[END OF QUESTION PAPER]

PRACTICE PAPER F

C

Paper 1

Non-calculator

Refer to page 3 for Instructions to Candidates

	KU	RE

1. Express $2\frac{1}{7}\%$ as a fraction in its lowest terms

    2

2. Evaluate $2\frac{2}{9} \times 4\frac{1}{5}$

    2

3. Evaluate $\sqrt{17^2 - 15^2}$

    2

4. Write down the gradient of the straight line whose equation is $y = 7x - 5$.

    1

5. (a) Solve $4(x - 1) < 3(x + 2)$

    2

   (b) Solve $3(8 - x) < 4(x - 1)$

    2

   (c) Hence solve $3(8 - x) < 4(x - 1) < 3(x + 2)$, expressing your answer in the form $a < x < b$.

    1

6. Express $\sqrt{125} + \dfrac{15}{\sqrt{5}}$ in the form $a\sqrt{b}$ where a and b are whole numbers.

4

7. A triangle may be specified by giving two angles and a side.

In $\triangle ABC$, c, $\hat{A}$ and $\hat{B}$ are known. The altitude CD of $\triangle ABC$ is drawn and has length h.

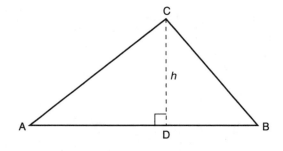

Express (i) AD in terms of h and $\hat{A}$;

    (ii) BD in terms of h and $\hat{B}$;

    (iii) h in terms of c, $\hat{A}$ and $\hat{B}$ in its simplest form.

2

2

2

8. Simplify $\dfrac{2x+5}{4x} - \dfrac{x-2}{2x+1}$

5

9. In a certain Swiss café, a Scottish family were charged 11·70 Swiss francs for three cups of coffee and two cups of tea, and a Welsh family were charged 14·20 Swiss francs for two coffees and four teas.

Assuming that the prices of the tea and coffee did not vary from one customer to another, find the cost of each.

5

10. *(a)* Factorise $a^2 - a - 12$

    (b) Hence factorise $(x + 2)^2 - (x + 2) - 12$

    (c) Hence, or otherwise, find two positive values of x for which $(x + 2)^2 - (x + 2) - 12$ is a multiple of 25.

11. Show that in this diagram

$$p : q = \sin^2 a : \sin^2 b.$$

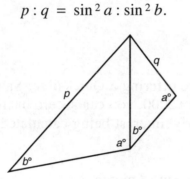

[END OF QUESTION PAPER]

51

Paper 2

Refer to page 3 for Instructions to Candidates

	KU	RE

1. A satellite is orbitting the earth in a circle of radius $4{\cdot}24 \times 10^3$ miles.

    Calculate, correct to three significant figures, the circumference of this circle, expressing your answer in standard form.

    2 (KU)

2. Dunnifax Building Society are offering a Quicksilver Savings Scheme whereby, if you invest at least £2000, you can secure interest of 9% per annum compounded half yearly, interest being calculated on complete pounds only.

    To how much would £2000 grow in 18 months?

    3 (KU)

3. In a class spelling test out of 25 marks, the boys' scores are illustrated by this frequency table.

Score	11	14	16	17	18	21	23
Frequency	1	1	3	5	2	1	1

    (a) Calculate the mean and standard deviation of the boys' scores.

    4 (KU)

    (b) There were equal numbers of boys and girls in this class. If the girls' scores had a mean of 18 and a standard deviation of $1{\cdot}83$, is the pupil with the highest score more likely to be a boy or a girl?

    2 (RE)

52

4. Modular structures based on a cube consist of rods and connectors as shown.

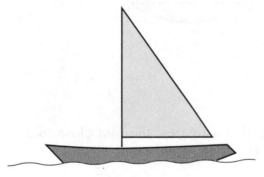

8 connectors
12 rods

12 connectors
20 rods

16 connectors
28 rods

(a) How many connectors and rods will be in the next structure in this sequence?

2

(b) How many connectors and rods will be in the 20th structure in this sequence?

4

5. The sail cloth for the sail on this boat cost £160. The sail cloth for a similar smaller boat cost £90.

The volume of the fuel tank in the larger boat is 24 cubic feet.

Calculate the volume of the fuel tank in the smaller boat.

3

6. (a) Factorise $p^2 - q^2$

1

(b) Hence factorise and simplify $(3 + 2\sqrt{5})^2 - (3 - 2\sqrt{5})^2$

2

7. An orienteer, starting at a car park C, makes first of all for a hotel H, 4 km away on a bearing of 140°. He then heads for a picnic site P which is 5 km away from H in the direction NE. Sketch ΔPHC, indicating the given distances and bearings.

Calculate how far the picnic site is from the car park.

5

8. Calculate the area of the shaded region shown.

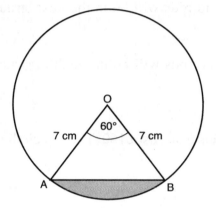

6

9. Find, correct to 3 significant figures, the root close to 1 of the cubic equation $2x^3 - 3x^2 + 4x - 5 = 0$.

5

10. The quadrangle of a certain university is in the shape of a square ABCD with a clock tower in the corner at C. The centre of the clock E is 19·7 m above C and its angle of elevation from A is 20°.

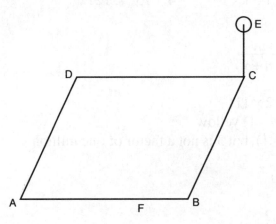

(a) Calculate

   (i) the length of the diagonal AC of the quadrangle   **3**

   (ii) the length of each side of the quadrangle.   **2**

(b) There is a side door into the University Chapel at F, which lies on AB such that $A\hat{C}F = 20°$.

Calculate

   (i) the length of FC   **3**

   (ii) the angle of elevation of E from F.   **3**

[END OF QUESTION PAPER]

ANSWERS

Practice Paper A — Paper 1

1. $6\cdot59$ 2. $4\frac{4}{15}$ 3. $1\cdot53\times10^9$ 4. $15, 4, 127$

5. $x<6$ 6. $\dfrac{2x}{x-3}$ 7. $\dfrac{uv}{u+v}$

8. *(a)* 11 red, 22 yellow ($22 = 2\times11$)
   (b) $(n+m-1)$ red, $2(n+m-1)$ yellow
   (c) False. Total $= 3(n+m-1)$, but 3 is not a factor of one million

9. $3''$ 10. $a=2, b=-60$

11. *(a)* 14   *(b)* $\dfrac{2}{5}$ *(c)* $\dfrac{2}{29}$

Paper 2

1. $x+2y=6$ 2. H.P. $=\dfrac{Tv}{550}$

3. 4 lengths @ $5\cdot6$ m $= 22\cdot4$ m   4. (i) $720°$ (ii) $120°$ (iii) $180°$

5. $26\,\text{cm}$ 6. $4, -8$ 7. $10\cdot12$ m

8. 3 years   9. $1\cdot2°, 0\cdot6°$

10. *(a)* Proof   *(b)* Proof   *(c)* $149\cdot3$

Practice Paper B — Paper 1

1. 18 & 19 **2.** 3 **3.** 10

4. $m = 11, p = 405$ **5.** 105 cm³ **6.** 18p

7. $a = 3, b = 40$

8. cum freq: 2 5 7 11 14 18 23 26 28 29

median = 34″, semi-interquartile range = $1\frac{1}{2}''$

9. $36\frac{1}{2}$

10. *(a)*

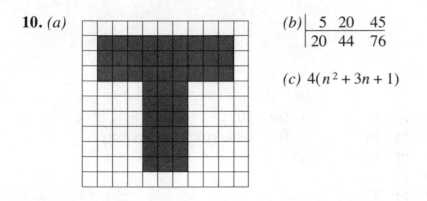

(b) $\begin{array}{|ccc} 5 & 20 & 45 \\ \hline 20 & 44 & 76 \end{array}$

(c) $4(n^2 + 3n + 1)$

11. *(a)* $\dfrac{2\sqrt{13}}{13}$ *(b)* 1 **12.** $y = 3 + 2x - x^2$

Paper 2

1. $x = 3, y = -4$ **2.** $\dfrac{pr}{p+1}$

3. *(a)* $I = \dfrac{1}{2}mr^2$ *(b)* $r_1 : r_2 = \sqrt{m_2} : \sqrt{2m_1}$ **4.** 70·5

5. $\dfrac{2}{x^2 - 4}$ **6.** *(a)* 3·87 km *(b)* 54 m *(c)* 0·63°

7. 1, 1·7 **8.** $\dfrac{-3}{4}$

9. *(a)* 180 *(b)* $2^3 \times 3 \times 7^2$ *(c)* 147 *(d)* 196 *(e)* 12 *(f)* 17 640

Practice Paper C — Paper 1

1. 64·9   **2.** $2\frac{1}{3}$ **3.** $\frac{3}{4}$ **4.** $x = -\frac{1}{2}, y = \frac{3}{4}$

5. $x = \pm \dfrac{\sqrt{a^2 w^2 - v^2}}{w}$ **6.** 275°   **7.** $9:4$

8. $a = -2, b = 2$ **9.** -3 **10.** 4

11. 20, 35   **12.** *(a)* $AD = h \sin \theta$; $BD = h \cos \theta$;   *(b)* Proof   *(c)* Proof

Paper 2

1. 8 inches, 18 inches

2. £78.81

3. *(a)*
rr	rb	rb	ry	ry	ry
br	bb	bb	by	by	by
br	bb	bb	by	by	by
yr	yb	yb	yy	yy	yy
yr	yb	yb	yy	yy	yy
yr	yb	yb	yy	yy	yy

   (b) 10   *(c)* same colour more likely

4. *(a)* $(-3, 0), (0, -15), (5, 0)$ *(b)* $(1, -16)$

5. 8138 m^2 **6.** 18·7 l **7.** 160 g   **8.** 4·0

9. *(a)* (i) 4   (ii) 49   (iii) 484
    (b) (i) 10   40   90   160   250   360   490   640   810   1000
        (ii) 9   36   81   144   225   324   484   625   784   961
    (c) conjecture is false (for $n \geq 7$)

Practice Paper D — Paper 1

1 20 & 21   **2.** 0·89   **3.** 9×10^3

4. The line passing through $(0, 1)$ and $(3, 3)$

5. 2π **6.** *(a)* $a + \dfrac{1}{a} + 2$ *(b)* $18\dfrac{1}{16}$

7. *(a)* $Q_1 = 8, Q_2 = 13·5, Q_3 = 28$ *(b)* mean $= 8$, S.D. $= 2\dfrac{2}{3}$

     (c) obviously better half has better mean and is also less spread out than lower half

8. $a = 3, b = 8$ **9.** 27 mm

10. *(a)* $(x - 4)(x - 25); 4, 25$ *(b)* $4, 25$
     (c) $x = 25$ is a solution, $x = 4$ is not
          $(\text{l.h.s.}) = -(\text{r.h.s.}) \Rightarrow (\text{l.h.s})^2 = (\text{r.h.s.})^2$
          i.e., $(4 - 10)^2 = (3\sqrt{4})^2$ but $4 - 10 \neq 3\sqrt{4}$

Paper 2

1. 7 years   **2.** $h = \dfrac{A - 2\pi r^2}{2\pi r}$ **3.** 3·1 nautical miles

4. *(a)* 27 ball joints, 54 tie rods   *(b)*

1	8	27	n^3
8	27	64	$(n + 1)^3$
12	54	144	$3n(n + 1)^2$

5. K.E of lorry $= \dfrac{1}{2}$ K.E. of car

6. *(a)* 25 cm²   *(b)* 300 cm³   *(c)* 6·45 kg   *(d)* 8

7. 18p   19p   28p   29p

8. $\dfrac{x^2 + 1}{(x - 1)^2}$ **9.** *(a)* 5·3 m   *(b)* 70°

10. Andrew's 100 cm, Billy's 80 cm   **11.** 5·5 cm

Practice Paper E — Paper 1

1 3·4   **2.** $3\frac{3}{7}$ **3.** $1\frac{2}{5}$ **4.** 8

5. 7   **6.** $5\sqrt{3}$

7.

W	5	4	4	3	3	3	2	2	2	1
D	0	1	0	2	1	0	3	2	1	4
L	0	0	1	0	1	2	0	1	2	0
P	15	13	12	11	10	9	9	8	7	7

8. $5\frac{1}{2}$ **9.** 810 ml   **10.** $g^{5/2}$

11. *(a)*

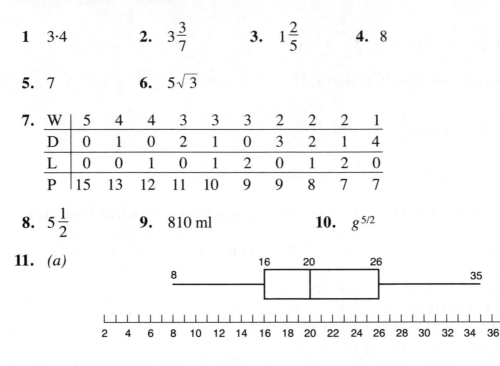

(b) there was a general improvement (median better by 7 strokes) but less players just failing to qualify (low scores being less spread out)

12. 160 kN   **13.** 5

Paper 2

1. 4 m²   **2.** $3\sqrt{10}$ **3.** $y^{11/6}$

4. *(a)* (i) $\dfrac{11}{160}$ (ii) $\dfrac{23}{40}$ *(b)* 140   **5.** 80·5°

6. $\dfrac{3(x+1)}{2(x-1)}$ **7.** *(a)* 2·86 m² *(b)* 6·13 m

8. *(a)* 1·5 (approx.) *(b)* 1·57

9. *(a)* 5·45 m *(b)* 3·50 m

10. *(a)* 40 m *(b)* $(16 + 8\sqrt{3})$ m² [29·9] *(c)* $\left(8 + \dfrac{8\sqrt{2}}{3}\right)$ m³ [11·77]

Practice Paper F — Paper 1

1. $\dfrac{3}{140}$
2. $9\dfrac{1}{3}$
3. 8
4. 7

5. (a) $x < 10$ (b) $x > 4$ (c) $4 < x < 10$
6. $8\sqrt{5}$

7. (i) $\dfrac{h}{\tan \hat{A}}$ (ii) $\dfrac{h}{\tan \hat{B}}$ (iii) $h = \dfrac{c \cdot \tan A \cdot \tan B}{\tan A + \tan B}$

8. $\dfrac{5(4x+1)}{4x(2x+1)}$
9. coffee 2·30 Swiss francs, tea 2·40 Swiss francs

10. (a) $(a+3)(a-4)$ (b) $(x+5)(x-2)$ (c) 20, 27 for example

11. Proof: use the Sine Rule for the common side, twice

Paper 2

1. $2·66 \times 10^4$ miles
2. £2282.33

3. (a) $17, 2·8$ (b) probably a boy since the girls' scores are less spread out

4. (a) 20 connectors and 36 rods   (b) 84 connectors and 164 rods

5. £90
6. (a) $(p-q)(p+q)$ (b) $24\sqrt{5}$

7.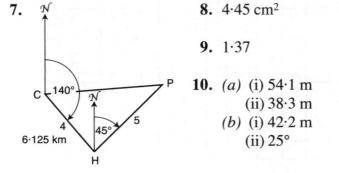

8. 4·45 cm²

9. 1·37

10. (a) (i) 54·1 m
    (ii) 38·3 m
    (b) (i) 42·2 m
    (ii) 25°

61

QUESTION ANALYSIS CHART

For candidates who wish to concentrate on a particular type of question rather than on a complete test, here is how to find the question of each type in this booklet. Some questions fall into more than one category.

Topic	A1	A2	B1	B2	C1	C2	D1	D2	E1	E2	F1	F2
non-calculator arithmetic	1,2		1,2		1,2,3		1,2		1,2,3		1,2,3	
standard form	3						3					1
growth and decay, compound interest						2		1				2
area / surface area / volume		3			12	6	9	6		10		
exhaustive lists								7	7			
statistics			8					7	11			3
probability	11					3				4		
number				9		9						
patterns & formulae	8		10		11			4				4
evaluation of a formula			9			8		11	4			
change of subject of formulae	7			2	5			2				
forming equations	9	8	6		10	7		10	13		9	
solving linear equations		8	3,6					11	5,13			
solving quadratic equations	9	6				4	10	10				
solving equations by iteration		10								8		9
linear inequalities	5									5		
interpreting graphs				7			8			8		
simultaneous equations				1	4	7					9	
quadratic functions & graphs			12			4						
factors and fractions	6			5				8		6	8,10	6
variation		2	4	3	7			5	12			
surds			11				5		6	2	6	
indices					9		6		10	3		
functional notation	4					9			8			
Pythagoras	11	5	11			1	5		6	2		10
y = mx + c		1		8			4			4		
arcs and sectors		10								7		8
angles and bearings		9		6	6			3				7
nets, similar shapes & solids			5		10			6	9	1		5
rt angle Δ trigonometry		9	11	6	12			9		5	7	10
trig equations, graphs, period	10	4	7	4	8							
sine rule		7		6				9			11	
cosine rule						5		3		9		7
area of Δ						5				9,10		

YOUR NOTES

YOUR NOTES

Printed by Bell & Bain Ltd., Glasgow, Scotland, U.K.